anne tallentire is an artist who has continuously addressed the shifting geographies, demographics and working practices of the displaced. she was born in n. ireland and has lived and worked in london since 1984. she is professor in fine art at central saint martins college of art and design.

object of a life is typeset in replica mono, designed by norm. the text is set in lowercase with reference to the german 'kleinschreibung' principle advocated by modernist designers, in particular max bill.

object of a life

anne tallentire

copy press

The Copy Press Limited
51 South Street
Ventnor
Isle of Wight
PO38 1NG

copypress.co.uk

Commune no. 5
Editor: Vit Hopley
Reader: Yve Lomax
Copy-editor: Sara Peacock
Design: Amerang

Printed on Munken Print White no.18 80gsm. Munken Print White standard products are FSCTM and PEFC certified.
Printed and bound in England.

A catalogue record for this book is available from the British Library

ISBN-13 978-0-9553792-7-7
ISBN-10 0-9553792-7-X

contents

introduction

'for when things are so disposed that, when they are presented to us through the senses, we can easily imagine them, and so easily remember them, we say that they are well ordered, but if the opposite is true, we say that they are badly ordered or confused.'

benedict de spinoza, *ethics*

gather/office

gather

breathing was difficult. she felt constrained. no one could see that she imagined her heart to be bound in non-toxic, lead-free, environmentally friendly, galvanised wire. but then no one noticed her. they were approaching fast, batons raised, and as one bore down, her world stalled. she stumbled and fell, legs and arms flailing.

the blackout was not total. as she hit the ground she saw patterns that resembled shadows sliding on the surface of the moon. she wondered if she could reach into her chest and pull her heart out. the whites of her eyes began to decrease in size. the amygdala – the almond-shaped structure in the forebrain associated with detection of fear – was at work.

in that hair-splitting moment he saw her panic and raised his baton to whack her skull. some minutes later, as the world came back into focus, she was sure she felt the wire that followed the contours of her heart begin to dissolve.

gather

in norway, during the second world war, the paper clip was worn by patriots as a symbol of defiance. the idea originated in france, where a paper clip was worn on a lapel or front pocket as a sign of resistance and opposition to german occupation. wearing one could lead to arrest, deportation or imprisonment, which contributed to its status as a symbol of solidarity.

there are numerous and conflicting accounts of the origin of the paper clip. the norwegian johan vaaler (1866–1910) was credited (erroneously according to some accounts) as the inventor in 1899. long after vaaler's death his compatriots erected, in his honour, a giant paper clip, seven metres high, on a college campus in oslo. america patented the paper clip in 1867, where it was initially used to attach tickets to fabric.

gather

the paper clip is in fact a piece of bent wire used for holding several sheets of paper together. it takes advantage of the elasticity and strength of the material of its construction, usually galvanised steel.

paper clips can be used as a device to reset compact disc players, to eject floppy discs from early computers and to remove sim cards from inside mobile phones. they have been used to pick locks and unpick handcuffs. the paper clip symbol has also been adopted universally as the icon to represent e-mail attachments, although these icons can be customised according to individual choice.

the production of novelty paper clips is increasing. occasionally the metal wire is covered in coloured plastic. in china, manufacturers are producing paper clips in the shape of flowers, animals or hearts.

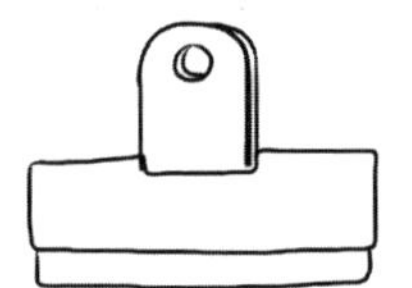

gather

the bulldog clip is made from a rectangular sheet of springy steel curved into a cylinder or folded into an isosceles triangle. flat strips of metal are inserted or attached to the cut edges of the steel to form two handles. when these handles are pressed together the jaws open against the force of the springiness forming a gap into which paper or card can be inserted. when the handles are released the clip springs shut to grip the load. bulldog clips vary in design and size: office foldback, quality foldback, 5 star grip, works essential, q connect, stainless steel and heavy duty. bulldog is a generalised term for the device.

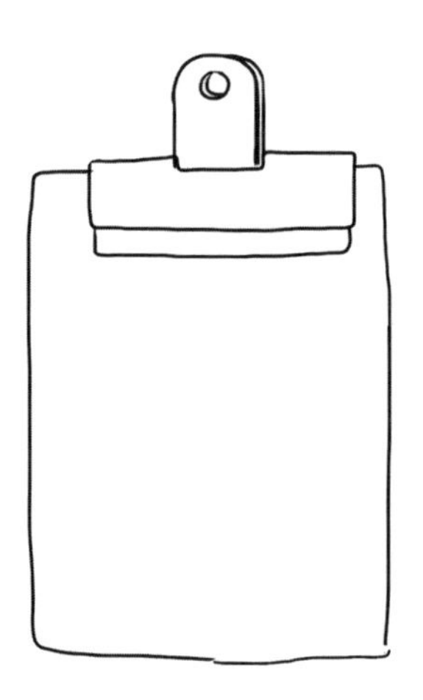

gather

bulldog clips are ideal to use when collating large amounts of paper. the paper can be removed quickly and easily although, if concentration is lost, the clip can suddenly spring shut and the papers can shift. prior to the invention of the bulldog clip the method of binding paper involved punching holes and threading with a tag of string.

louis e. baltzley from washington, was attributed with the invention in 1910. he invented the clip to help his father, a writer and inventor, hold his manuscripts together easily.

the bulldog clip is often used when displaying drawings. i have used it in the studio to attach a construction worker's glove to a sheet of orange perspex and a laminated panel with a red melamine finish.

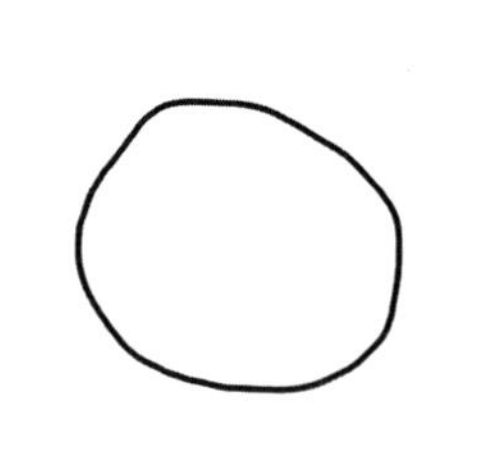

gather

a circle of expanding matter is stretched to its limit. she wears the band as a reminder to go to the market. it is red. faded. she keeps the band hanging on a nail next to the kitchen door, along with the keys to her house and a black-and-white chequered foldaway shopping bag. she believes that wearing it helps corral her thoughts and will remind her to buy the things she needs.

at the market, she spends an inordinate length of time gazing at the flowers arranged in buckets displayed upon upturned wooden planks resting on grey plastic beer crates. she finally selects a bunch of cornflowers. her favourite. as she holds them close to her face to inspect the tight blue petals in an effort to determine the health of the blooms, drops of water fall from the tips of the stems onto her wrist. she reaches forward to pay, her arm raised, and a cold stream trickles slowly all the way up to her elbow.

gather

there are no seats. she will have to sit on her suitcase between carriages. it is difficult to write in these circumstances. the curve of the nib is short and abrupt. it digs into the paper. the blue-black ink is deposited from the narrow channel that runs between two microscopic ridges. a knock to the elbow or indeed the slightest breath could blow it off course, sending it careering across the page and streaming into competing tributaries. but given the thickness of the paper, the ink would not get far. it would quickly peter out and seep into the paper, drying as a brittle stain.

spread/street

spread

in a farmyard, near albarese, in southern tuscany, the moon is shifting in the grey sky. a cat scratches at the legs of a chair. if she leans back, she will fall. so she stands to move the chair closer to the wall. she sits back down again, stretches her legs and tilts her head back. the stars are bright. she traces a route from mercury to jupiter, drawing detours with her eyes that take her off towards the andromeda galaxy. she imagines a plumb line running from saturn to the earth below her feet.

across the yard she notices a discarded bicycle propped against a wire fence. at the far end of the shed a length of electric cable dangles from the roof and casts a shadow on the wall. the cable's rubber casing has perished. as clouds gather, the yard becomes soaked in a charcoal wash. it flows over the bicycle, the cable and the grain of the gravel, paying no attention to gaps or hollows. when finally she stands up to go back to the house a thread of light catches the top of her head.

spread

it is morning. a comb snags and pulls on her knotted hair. sitting bolt upright facing the wall, she braces herself. the wall bears a trellis of cracks that map years of neglect.

spread

the entrance to the park is blocked. it has been raining. the camp has all but gone. the few remaining tents are empty. a matrix of tent pegs can be seen just proud of the mud. there was no particular system here, nothing imposed, rather more a practice of improvisation.

every evening there was a programme of events, lectures, performances and screenings; discussions that brought objects into question, in relation to economics, politics, ecology, work, politics and love.

someone named the field ‘the think camp’.

spread

she is proud of her new black patent brogues. they came in a box that has since been commissioned for storing those things that have no place yet. they take her out, past the industrial estate at the end of the street. she walks quickly, reading the signs as she goes. at the cross roads there are road works. she stalls. there is an irritating hole in the heel of the sock. the right-hand foot.

spread

a follows b. a is transfixed by the yellow violin case strapped to b's back. the case is covered in travel stickers from japan, australia, germany, estonia, new york, nigeria, manchester, geneva and argentina. it is a long walk up from the metro. finally, they arrive at the main concourse having passed shops, arcades and food stalls. a keeps with b all the way to the upper level. the 14.47 eurostar approaches at platform 3. b stands by the barrier craning her neck to view the passengers disembark. it takes 24 minutes for the platform to clear. a watches b as she drinks a coffee. no one arrives for her. a walks back across the concourse to platform 11 to catch her train.

b moves to platform 7 to await the 15.59 thalys service from brussels. she waits. then, before heading back to platform 3 for the 17.17 from london, she stops to lean against the base of one of the iron pillars that support the building. still no one arrives. she moves along to wait at platform 9 for the high speed tgv from flanders and lille due at 18.44. she searches the crowd, then treads back down to platform 30 on the level below to meet the suburban beauvais trains. finally she makes her way towards the metro platforms beneath the eastern end of the station to wait for the last train from the airport at 00.15, from where a, who has left, arrived. later, at 02.00, b covers her violin case with her jacket and lies down on the stone step, out of the wind.

spread

the ironwork screens the balcony. the windows behind have been decorated with transparent coloured film cut out to depict stylised leaves. it looks like the texture of skin suffering some distressing condition. building works are reflected in the spaces between the leaves, collapsing the whole block in a complex mirroring.

spread

her thoughts float on the still, stagnant, green-blue pond water.

spread

polarised plugs reduce the risk of electric shock and fire.

stack/industry

stack

concentration was lost when the plate was dropped. it was the last. a calcified bubble and some undulations in the ceramic interrupted the cold flat surface. perhaps there had been a problem with the cooling temperature or the surface tension of the glaze. at any rate that bubble looked like a crater in the making. one thing was clear. the working hours had been too long, illegal even, and conditions unbearable. a strike was inevitable.

that plate was always stored at the bottom of the pile, on the top shelf. it was seldom used and never put down for anyone else. it would not have been thrown away because on those occasions when it appeared from the bottom of the pile it brought to mind shallow waves over sand, the leaves of a white orchid and days of resistance.

stack

they were aligned almost perfectly and the weight of each of the fifteen equally distributed. when viewed from a distance, the uninterrupted surface of each unit could have been mistaken momentarily for steps. steps that had folded back on themselves. but when viewed at an angle, the interlocked metal legs of the chairs rippled. stacked to the same height, approximately 10 feet tall, only one unit had incurred the instability of a probable collapse.

stack

the rain has softened the boxes and made this one heavier. flattened. it now takes some effort to lift. the pink plastic string that binds the bundle leaves a pale red mark across the palm. the boxes had contained summer cotton dresses. dresses with red dots, lozenge patterns in green and black, sizes: 12, 14, 16, 18, 20, 22 uk. made in china. bound for the market. the foam offcuts, lying across it: pale pink, grey, blue. the recycling truck is late.

stack

this stone has been quarried some time back. the yard is well ordered; there are slabs and setts for paving. there are all manner of shapes and colours, but those dug up on the streets of barcelona were plain granite and heavy to throw.

stack

in the alley, between the two rows of houses, eight slates are propped outside the back door to number 4. a square of toffee is sandwiched between two of the slates. when it is hot the toffee melts, but it is cold and the toffee is brittle. the roof is covered in a silver waterproof membrane secured with a grid of wooden batons. it begins to rain.

girls walk past below. they shake a can of coke that spills fizz over the slate, leaving behind a sticky pattern of cloud.

stack

blue, yellow, blue again, yellow and blue. azure, white and cobalt blue. you could hardly call it a fountain, that spluttering thing. it has been installed directly opposite the courthouse. the base is granite. the façade of the courthouse is covered in ultramarine flame-retardant scaffold sheeting. it billows.

stack

thick liquid is advancing towards the edge of a black lacquered tray. the tray is painted with images of birds entwined with fronds of fern and flowers that she thinks might be the stralitza orchid; red caribea, otherwise known as caribbean red pepper; musa coccinea, commonly known as scarlet banana or red flowering banana; heliconia pisttacorum, also known as parrot's beak, parakeet flower or false bird of paradise. she discovers she can buy seeds for all these varieties.

the liquid crawls a little faster now. it has almost covered the surface but cadmium red and turquoise beaks peek through here and there. she contemplates this scene for a while before dipping her finger into the liquid to draw a line around a leaf of the stalitiza. as she does so the rest of the viscous mess slides to the edge, blurring everything else.

tilt/studio

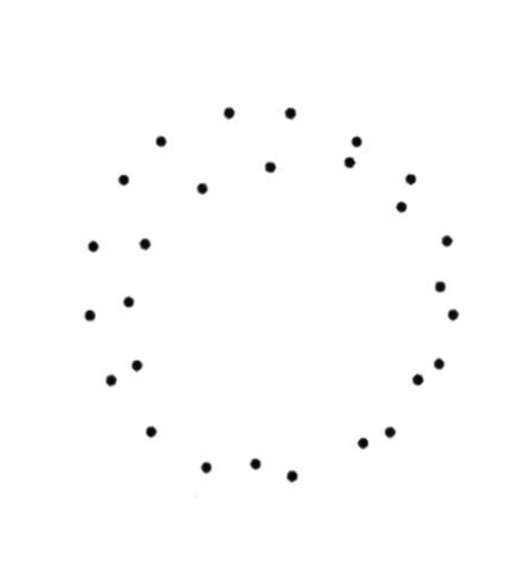

tilt

everyone is star gazing these days. there are telescopes everywhere. on balconies, roof tops and in back gardens. and then, at the other end of the scale, there is the loupe.

a loupe is a device used to magnify small things. a lens is contained within a cylindrical cone above a dome of glass. it was invented and manufactured in germany in the eighteenth century by the optical company leica. wátchmakers, photographers, engineers, tattoo artists, jewellers, dentists, surgeons, biologists, scientists, philatelists and artists use different types of loupe.

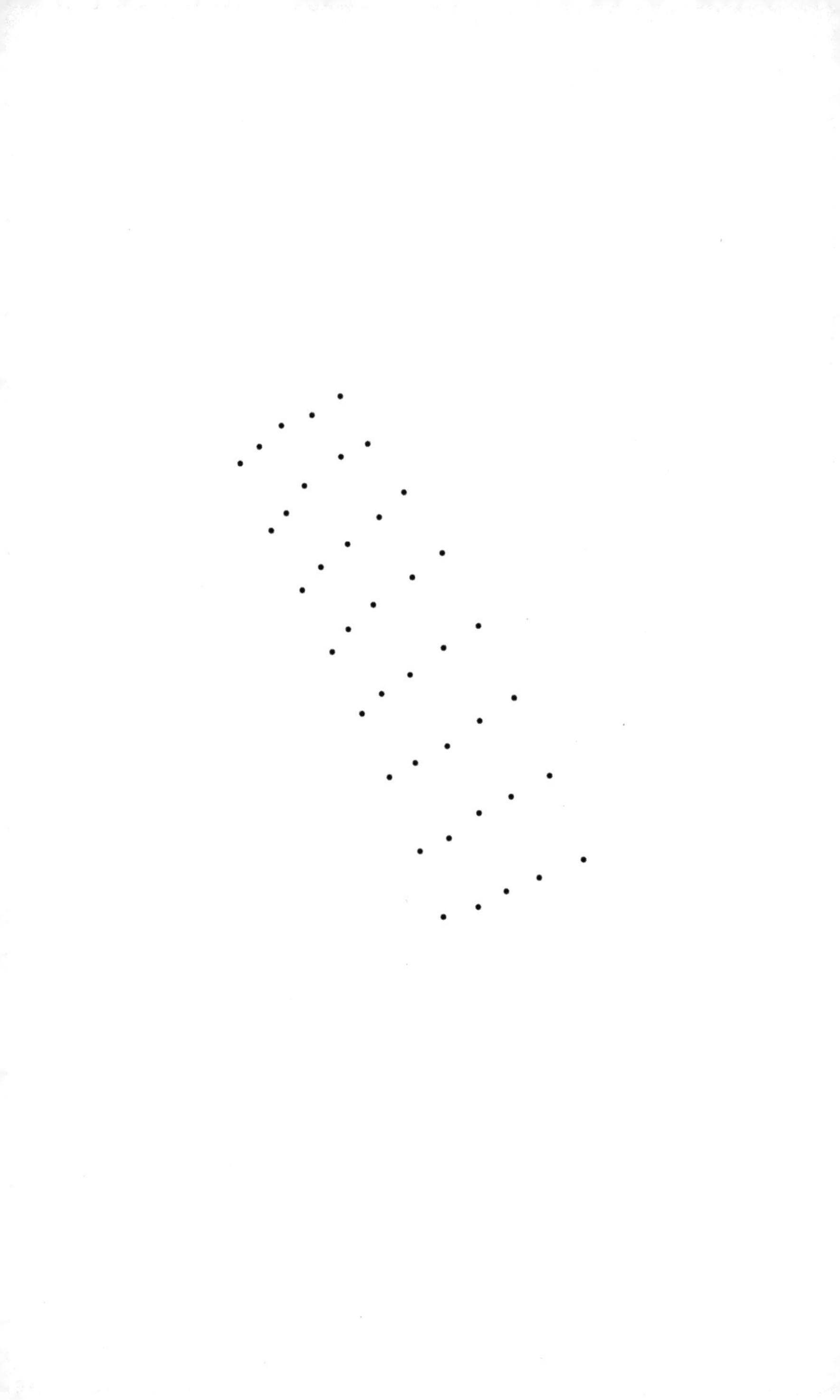

tilt

take the stylus and mark rows of dots in parallel diagonal lines from edge to edge across the surface of the screen. the lines will make a track from top left to bottom right. it is vital that an attempt is made to place the dots equally. it is necessary to take care not to swipe the surface with a cuff of the sleeve, otherwise a trail of unruly marks will interrupt the pattern.

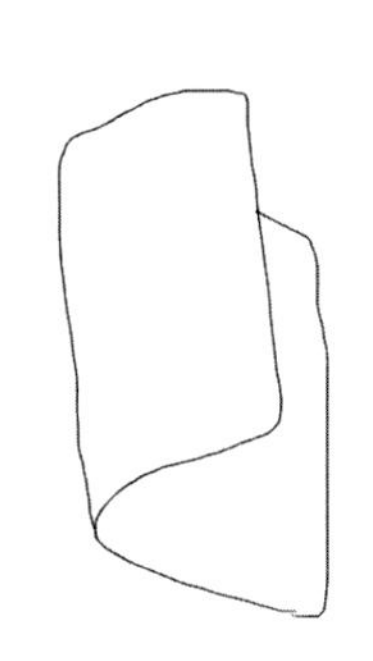

tilt

unfixed. it is going to take some doing to find a suitable container for these awkward shapes. volume is a problem. perhaps this is the time to let some of it go. organise in rows according to size, shape and length of service.

if i were you, i would be careful when deciding what to discard. on the other hand, why not just let it go?

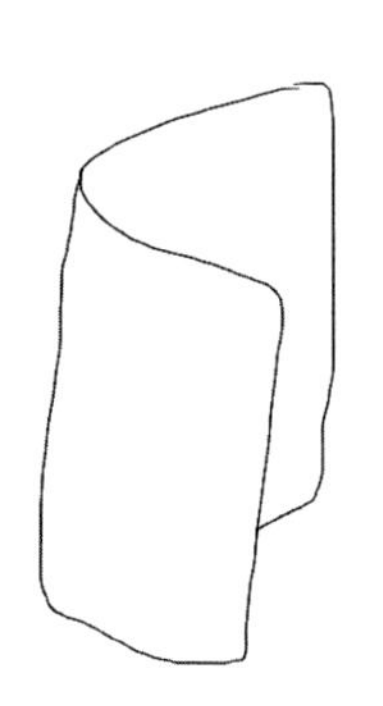

tilt

there is no rehearsal for this performance. it consists of one task. to assess the level of each object in the room using a spirit level, and to find one thing that lies true.

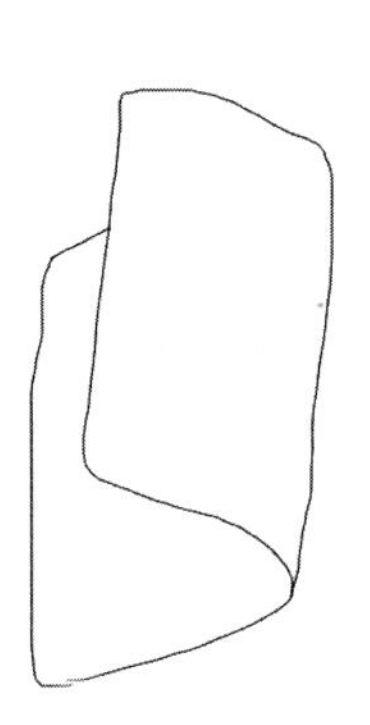

tilt

threading film into a projector takes practice; it takes skill to find the first sprocket. the projectionist living in the projection booth considers the art of mourning and the time of forgetting. miles of film are spliced and loaded. sound is adjusted during projection, and everyday maintenance of the equipment is carried out with meticulous precision.

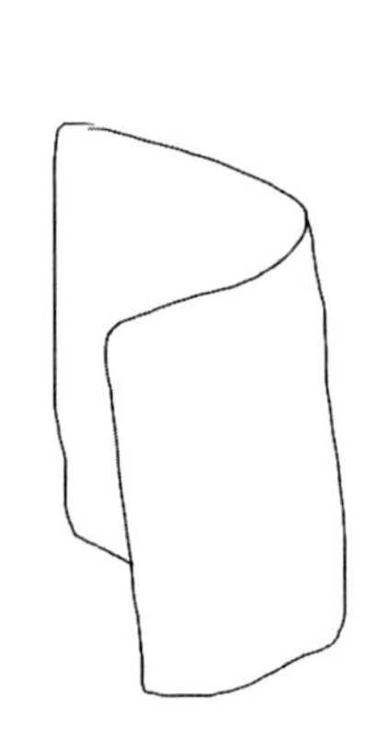

tilt

on the grey concrete floor there are twelve 5-millimetre-thick aluminium metal offcuts placed on a sheet of block board, which is lying on plastic roofing material. there are two trestle tables at the opposite end. the one used for drawing is currently covered in photographs. it sits beneath the windows. the window ledges are deep and faced with metal. four chairs, a ladder and a stool are scattered through the space. large panels are stored against the wall on the right and portfolios lean against the back of two filing cabinets. propped in the far corner there are rolls of drawing paper.

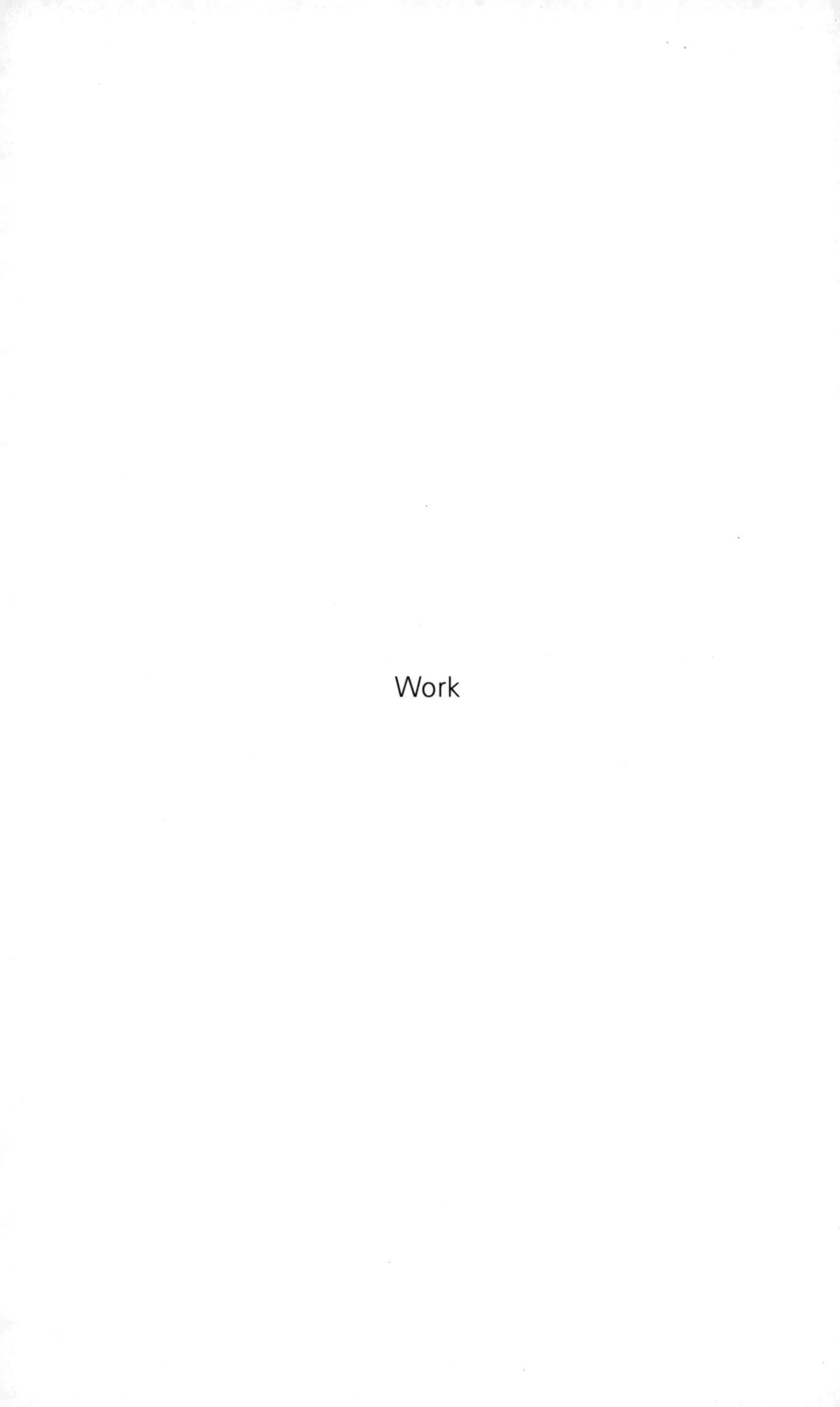

Work

tilt

it looks like a regular ballpoint pen. it arrived by post in a makeshift box made from two rectangular pieces of white polystyrene sandwiched together and secured lightly at each end with wide soft-stick masking tape. the pen sits in a channel cut into the thicker of the two pieces of polystyrene. the thinner piece forms the lid of the box. the pen is black and cream with a push-button mechanism and two transparent windows on either side of the barrel. when the button is repeatedly pressed the word 'work' appears and disappears in the windows of the pen. rotating.
the note accompanying the gift reads:

this disappeared on me for a few years. then i found it a few weeks ago. i scratched the word risk from it. i could not find a way to make it into art.   perhaps by giving it to you.

i take the pen from the box and begin to think of labour, time and friendship. this is a refillable pen. the writing sphere is steel but the ink is dry.

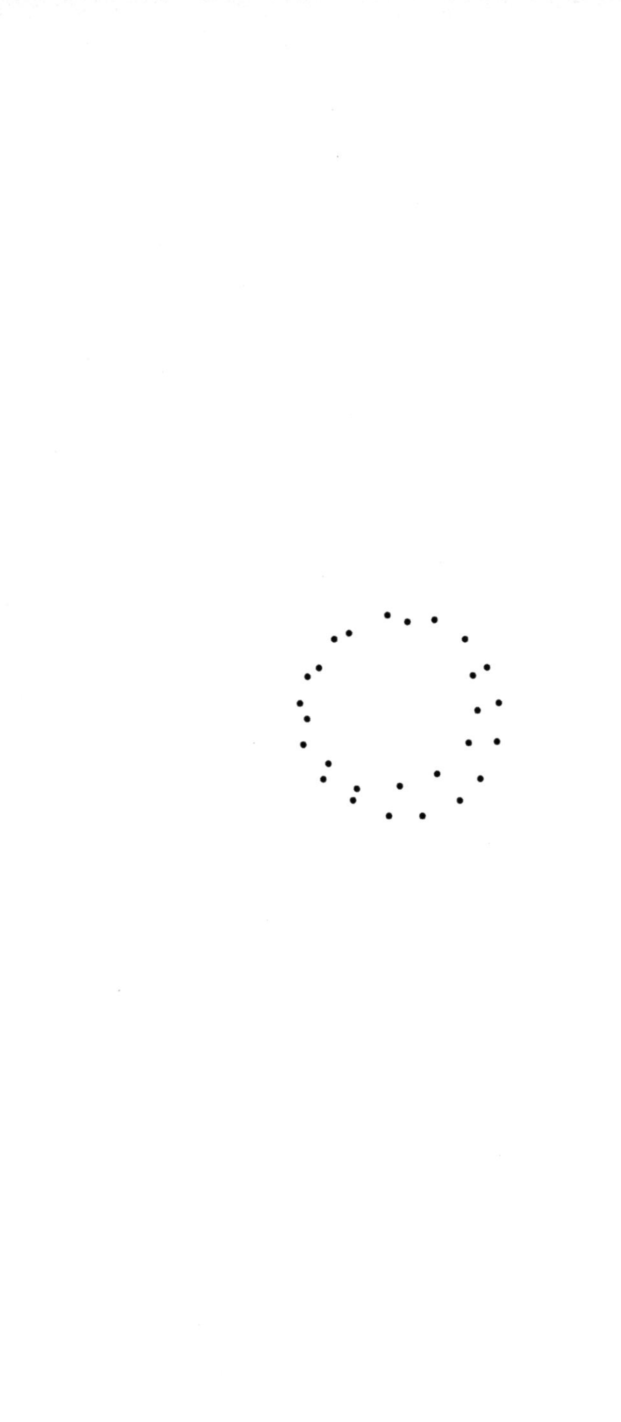

tilt

it is cold. the edge of the loupe cupped around the eye is creating a red rim above the eyebrow and a streak across the left cheekbone. an ice cube is melting inside the glass dome. water seeps out. the experiment is going to plan. a rectangle of light inside the semicircle of glass seems fixed, but the dome is full of a fractured image: black, grey and white. it rolls. later with the right eye sealing the viewing chamber, the eyelashes get in the way. they brush the edge. one edge recedes as the other comes into view.

leave/shelter

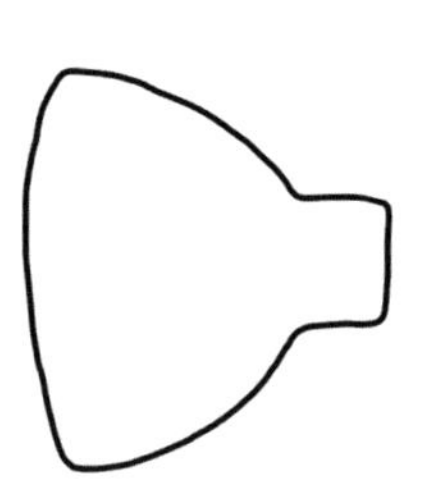

leave

she is asking herself what constitutes an encounter. while thinking about this she walks into a building full of people. she recognises a few faces but knows no one by name. she looks around and considers whom she might speak to. eventually she finds the courage to walk towards a woman who is standing slightly apart from a small group. she feels awkward but manages to stammer a greeting of sorts.

then, as she speaks, it is as though her breath solidifies and her voice morphs into a weird three-dimensional form that floats out from her, through the air, to the far side of the room. it hits the wall opposite with some force before bouncing back to exactly where she is standing. she reaches up, and amazed at the speed of her reflexes, catches it. noticing how smooth and cold it is she hands it to the stranger.

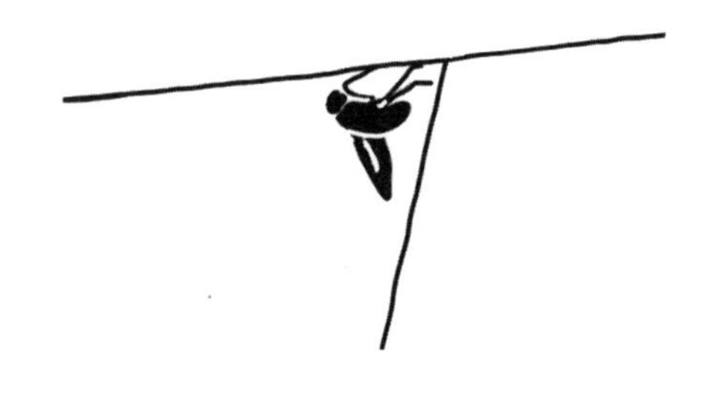

leave

she withdrew from the popular stage and began to study insects. it began when she was writing at her kitchen table. she heard them above her head, buzzing around in the corners of the sloping glass roof.

the musca domestica, most common of all flies, known more generally as the housefly, is her favourite. it is grey with two wings, is 14 centimetres long, is bred on dead organic matter and lives for approximately three weeks. female houseflies are slightly larger than males. they feed on liquid and fly by day and rest by night. they congregate on windows, in corners of rooms and semi-dark places. she watches them hover, circle and dive, and studies how they land. she notices how they like to be around human beings and animals.

lately, she discovered the azure damselfly. it has exquisite filigree. however, it is this housefly that captivates her.

leave

‘just wait’, she said, ‘just a minute please. i need to check something’. she went back to the house, rummaged in her rucksack, unlocked the door and, leaving it ajar, ran into the kitchen. there it was, on the table. she had planned to take it with her, but now that she was late she wondered if she should go at all.

they had spent months looking for a room by applying a system of random selection. with eyes closed, they would mark a spot on the map, travel there, buy the local paper and view the first property listed. this threw up some pitiful abodes, damp, filthy and overpriced.

she stared at a fleck of paint that had fallen on to the sleeve of her coat as she had left the last property. now the island of solidified paint lay on her kitchen table and she began to flick it around with her knife. it consisted of three layers of colour: magnolia, blue and grey.

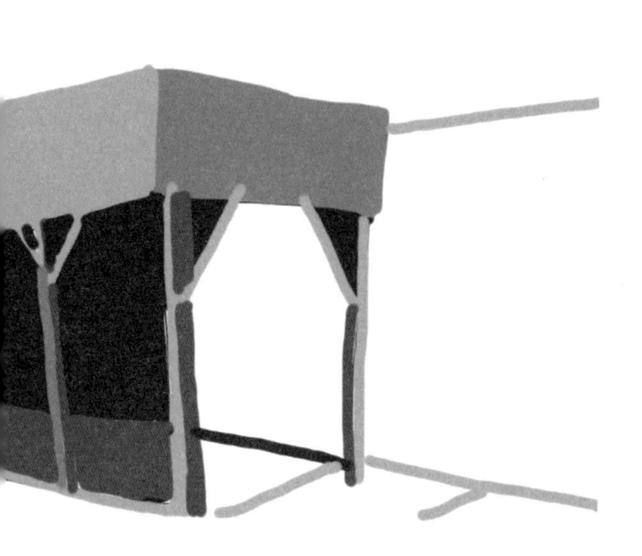

leave

downtown eastside was where we were going when i realised that the living conditions we had been enduring could get no worse. so, we would stay on 4th street, greenwich village. she introduced me to someone who had known the writer djuana barnes, and we went to have tea in the apartment where she had lived. i remember the warm living room and the sink.

the apartment we found was cold and damp and the neighbourhood was stretched and drawn together with telegraph wires that were full of chatter. the square was better than the street; everyone looked in towards the park.

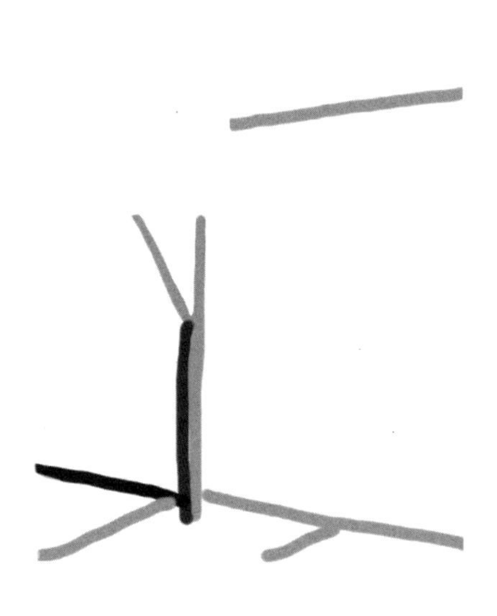

leave

his front tooth is cracked and one third of it is missing. he told me he had crashed into a wall on new year’s eve. he had searched everywhere but he could not find the missing triangle of tooth that had broken off. the floor, a highly polished concrete, ran flush against the walls. there were no cracks or gullies into which the fragment of tooth might have fallen. and now part of him was lost.

leave

the metallic button that fell off the sleeve of a black plastic jacket had lain for months in dust underneath the radiator. it now resides in a bowl with loose change and shines beneath the glass roof reflecting light from the sun by day and the moon by night. however, when the stars are hidden in rain and above the clouds, the button recedes from view and identification of any kind is impossible.

leave

what does it resemble, this perfectly formed thing? we are not sure but it presents a problem. it is so clean and fragile and we dare not touch it for fear of leaving a mark. it is 12 centimetres in diameter. glass. it is placed upon a white coffee table.

it is an evening in august and the time has arrived to eat translucent white noodles, green beans and leeks curling in small semicircles flavoured with mint and lemon. underneath the table: a yellow-brown nicotine stain, scribbles and faded football stickers look like nothing to the naked eye, but mean everything to her.

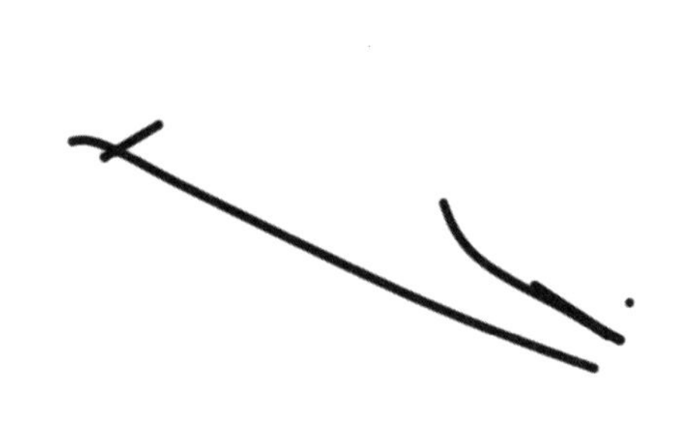

leave

the tree outside the window casts a shadow that marks the surface of the screen. although at first glance the image appears to be flat and static, it cannot conceal what occurs here. it is necessary to move with vigilance and apply a principle of spontaneity within the constraints of the given structure. working from the first mark to the last, taking what comes and running with it, she moves between one and the other, through and between the limit of the thing and the life of the object.

Common Intellectual series

Current Editions

1 *Wednesday Afternoon*
Vit Hopley

2 *Paris*
Michael Schwab

3 *Revisiting the Bonaventure Hotel*
Jaspar Joseph-Lester

4 *Common*
Hayley Newman

5 *Object of a Life*
Anne Tallentire

Future Editions

For future editions, please visit the Copy Press website

Copy Press is committed to bringing readers and writers together and invites you to join its Reader's Union – please visit www.copypress.co.uk